★ *BE WISE! Order several sets*
Book Club's GIFT BOX OF B
It's a wonderful bargain!

To W & G FOYLE LTD 119-125 Charing Cross Road London WC2

   Please send me the undermentioned Books for which

   I enclose £   :   :   to

   cover their cost plus postage.

Books value £2 and over sent Carriage Paid in Great Britain.

TITLE	£	s.	d.

Name..
    (BLOCK LETTERS PLEASE)

Address ....

....

REYNARD PRESS, FLITCROFT STREET, W.C.2

MORE BOOK CLUB SELECTIONS FOR CHRISTMAS GIFTS

MICKEY SPILLANE
ONE LONELY NIGHT

Mike Hammer, America's most popular private eye, in an exciting new skirmish. Published at 8s. 6d.

3s. 6d. (postage 6d.)

LADIES WON'T WAIT by Peter Cheyney. A hard-hitting mystery story in the best Peter Cheyney style. Published at 8s. 6d.

3s. 6d. (postage 6d.)

DEATH IN DARK GLASSES by George Bellairs. Murder, impersonation, forgery and embezzlement — these are the ingredients of this splendid thriller. Published at 9s. 6d.

3s. 6d. (postage 6d.)

MONICA DICKENS
My Turn to Make the Tea

A witty, lively and thoroughly entertaining book. "Brilliant"— **Punch.** Published at 12s. 6d.

3s. 6d. (postage 6d.)

RENNY'S DAUGHTER by Mazo de la Roche. A delightful new addition to the chronicles of the famous Whiteoak family. Published at 12s. 6d.

3s. 6d. (postage 6d.)

THE MOST REMARKABLE ADVENTURE STORY OF OUR TIMES!

★  ★

EXPEDITION

by
Thor Heyerdahl

The spectacularly successful story of a thrill-packed, true-life adventure on board a primitive raft. A stimulating combination of dare-devil courage, forethought and resourcefulness. Published at 12s. 6d.

3s. 6d. (postage 6d.)

A FINE BIOGRAPHY
H. G. WELLS

by Vincent Brome

An unconventional biography of H. G. Wells and a brilliant characterisation of the man and his work. Published at 15s.

3s. 6d. (postage 6d.)

JOY STREET

by
Frances Parkinson Keyes

A long, colourful, crowded novel. Published at 12s. 6d.

3s. 6d. (postage 6d.)

THESE BOOK CLUB BOOKS MAKE SPLENDID GIFTS

SOME OF THE FAMOUS FOYLES HANDBOOKS

All at **2/6** Each

(postage 3d.)

Aquariums

Home Carpentry

Modelling

Fruit Growing

Ice Hockey

Home Decorating

Cycling

Judo

Lampshade Making

Photography

Conjuring

Sailing

Rabbit Keeping

Wood Finishing

Puppetry

Card Conjuring

Sketching Out-of-Doors

Artificial Flower Making

Basketry

Full list on request

BOOK CLUB SELECTIONS

FOR CHRISTMAS GIFTS

J. B. Priestley's
DELIGHT

A grand collection of heartwarming essays with Mr. Priestley in his best forthright, round-the-fireside mood. A book to read again and again. Published at 10s. 6d.

3s. 6d. (postage 6d.)

NEVIL SHUTE
THE FAR COUNTRY

Nevil Shute's great best-selling novel of Australian life. A first-rate story of heart-warming humanity, of love, loyalty and courage. Published at 12s. 6d.

3s. 6d. (postage 6d.)

STEAMBOAT GOTHIC

by Frances Parkinson Keyes
A long, exciting story of the fabulous Louisiana plantation country. Published at 13s. 6d.

3s. 6d. (postage 6d.)

DEATH CASTS NO SHADOW by P. G. Larbalestier. A spine-chilling mystery story. Published at 8s. 6d.

3s. 6d. (postage 6d.)

THE GRAND SOPHY by Georgette Heyer. An exciting historical novel. Published at 10s. 6d.

3s. 6d. (postage 6d.)

ANYBODY CAN DO ANYTHING

A boisterous collection of reminiscences by the author of **The Egg and I.** Packed tight with laughs, and a-bubble with good humour. Published at 10s. 6d.

3s. 6d. (postage 6d.)

A TERRACE IN THE SUN by Cecil Roberts. A thoroughly absorbing novel by one of the most popular of contemporary writers. Published at 12s. 6d.

3s. 6d. (postage 6d.)

FOOTSTEPS IN CIVILISATION

F. KINGDON-WARD
A short history of civilisation inspired by the author's studies of tribal customs and manners in the Himalayas, Assam, Burma and Western China, as well as general conditions elsewhere. Published at 12s. 6d.

3s. 6d. (postage 6d.)

Two Splendid Westerns
FLAMING IRONS

by Max Brand

TEXAS GUN LAW

by Gladwell Richardson

each 3s. 6d. (post. 6d.)

CLASSICS BOOK CLUB EDITIONS
of these great books

Attractively bound and printed.   3s. 6d. each

(postage 6d.)

NEWS FROM NOWHERE
by William Morris

GREEN MANSIONS
by W. H. Hudson

AMARYLLIS AT THE FAIR
by Richard Jefferies

THE COMPLEAT ANGLER
by Izaak Walton

GULLIVER'S TRAVELS
by Jonathan Swift

THE HOUSE WITH THE GREEN SHUTTERS
by George Douglas

THE HOUSE OF THE SEVEN GABLES
by Nathaniel Hawthorne

TRAVELS WITH A DONKEY
by Robert Louis Stevenson

BLACK BEAUTY
by Anna Sewell

THESE BOOK CLUB BOOKS MAKE SPLENDID GIFTS

RECOMMENDED
BOOKS
FOR MEN

THE EDDIE CHAPMAN STORY by Frank Owen. British-born Eddie Chapman was trained by the Nazis as a spy and saboteur. This is the story of his sensational adventures as a spy and counter-spy.

10s. 6d. (postage 5d.)

SEA HUNTERS by Frank Robb. A grand adventure novel of deep-sea line-fishing in the coral forests of the great Mozambique Current.

10s. 6d. (postage 5d.)

JIVARO by Bertrand Flornoy. Adventures among the head-shrinkers of the Amazon. Illustrated.

15s. (postage 8d.)

PUBLISH AND BE DAMNED! by Hugh Cudlipp. The astonishing story of the " Daily Mirror " and a behind-the-scenes record of the growth of the newspaper that shocked Fleet Street.

12s. 6d. (postage 1s.)

ARNHEM LIFT by Louis Hagen. The story of the First British Airborne Division's great fight to hold the Arnhem Bridge, as seen and experienced by one of the glider pilots who took a distinguished part in the fighting. Illustrated.

8s. 6d. (postage 3d.)

FLAMINGO HUNT by Paul A. Zahl. The lively account of a scientist's adventurous search in remote Bahamas waters for the nesting grounds of the pink flamingo.

10s. 6d. (postage 5d.)

THE BOMBARD STORY by Alain Bombard. The vivid account of Dr. Bombard's single-handed Atlantic crossing in a rubber dinghy, during which he proved it is possible to live entirely off the sea for 65 days.

12s. 6d. (postage 9d.)

SEVEN YEARS IN TIBET by Heinrich Harrer. Incredible adventures in country never before traversed by a white man. A graphic study of Tibet and Tibetans.

16s. (postage 9d.)

THE MAN WHO NEVER WAS by Ewen Montagu. The fantastic — but true — story of the British Secret Service's brilliant coup which completely deceived the German High Command and ensured the success of the Allied landing in Sicily.

10s. 6d. (postage 6d.)

The Famous Children's TV Favourite
HANK'S CAMERA CAPERS
By Francis Coudrill

Remarkable value! Illustrated on every page with magnificent photographs and drawings in full colour.

2s. 6d. (postage 6d.)

F. MAURICE SPEED
FILM REVIEW

A complete record of the year's films with nearly 400 illustrations of stars and scenes and many extra-special features.

12s. 6d. (postage 1s.)

GILBERT HARDING
Along My Line

The forthright life-story of Britain's most-talked-about radio and television personality. (Publication November 23rd.)

12s. 6d. (postage 6d.)

A " Listen with Mother " Book
SPRING, SUMMER, AUTUMN & WINTER

Edited by JEAN SUTCLIFFE

Stories, games and rhymes for the very young. Published by special arrangement with the B.B.C.

5s. (postage 6d.

EVE GARNETT

THE FAMILY FROM ONE END STREET

The book which won the Library Association's Carnegie Medal for the Best Children's Book of the Year. It's a lovely, laughable story of the ups and downs of life in the Ruggles family.

6s. (postage 6d.)

WONDERFUL VALUE!

THE LITTLE GOLDEN BOOKS

All of the titles in this brilliant series of children's books are beautifully produced in lavish colour. " I think these books are absolutely excellent " —**Wilfred Pickles**. " An enchanting series with an immediate appeal to the young child "—**Enid Blyton.**

HOPALONG CASSIDY AND
BAR-20 COWBOY

NURSERY SONGS

ABC

NURSERY RHYMES

NIGHT BEFORE CHRISTMAS

STORY OF JESUS

PRAYERS FOR CHILDREN

THE COLOUR KITTENS

THE JOLLY BARNYARD

THE FUZZY DUCKLING

THE SHY LITTLE KITTEN

THE SAGGY BAGGY
ELEPHANT

MR. NOAH & HIS FAMILY

OUR PUPPY

THE SEVEN SNEEZES

THE THREE BEARS

KATIE THE KITTEN

each 2s. 6d. (postage 2d.)

GIRL'S BOOK OF BALLET

edited by A. H. FRANKS

A gala volume consisting of contributions by ballerinas and ballet writers, with nearly 200 magnificent action photographs and drawings and a comprehensive list of ballet terms.

12s. 6d. (postage 1s.)

Picture-Story Adaptation of

BLACK BEAUTY

An outstanding new picture-story adaptation of Anna Sewell's beloved Black Beauty. Excellent illustrations in colour and monochrome.

4s. 6d. (postage 6d.)

Also available in this series:—

**ROBINSON CRUSOE   HEIDI
THE STORY OF HIAWATHA
THE WIZARD OF OZ
MOTHER GOOSE**

each 4s. 6d. (postage 6d.)

STILL-WATER ANGLING

by RICHARD WALKER

British Empire record-holder Richard Walker—in 1952 he caught a 44lb. carp—is an angler with some remarkable new theories and in this book he sets down his successful technique. Many photographs and sketches.

18s. (postage 6d.)

A CHILD'S BOOK OF

HORSES

by E. Joseph Dreany

A delightful book for boys and girls aged five to nine. Beautifully illustrated; attractive binding.

2s. (postage 3d.)

PARIS CUISINE

by James Beard and Alexander Watt
A mouth-watering collection of delightful French recipes, combined with a unique guide to sixty French restaurants—ranging from fashionable Maxims to unpretentious bistros.

15s. (postage 6d.)

GEORGE CANSDALE'S

ZOO BOOK

Television's George Cansdale presents a fascinating close-up of the animal kingdom and the world of birds and fishes. "Zoo Book" includes over 70 wonderful pictures—brilliantly photographed and a joy to look at.

8s. 6d. (postage 6d.)

CAPTAIN PETER CHURCHILL

DUEL OF WITS

The story of Captain Peter Churchill's experiences as an organiser of Resistance and a remarkable account of the hour-to-hour existence of a secret agent. It makes remarkable reading.

12s. 6d. (postage 5d.)

GERANIUMS

by DEREK CLIFFORD

A lucid and informative handbook. The author grows what is probably the world's largest collection of geranium varieties. Illustrated.

5s. (postage 3d.)

THE BALLET ANNUAL
1954

Edited by Arnold L. Haskell

A splendid record of an outstanding year of ballet activity. It includes well over 100 photographs and numerous authoritative articles. The beautiful full-colour picture jacket portrays Margot Fonteyn in "Swan Lake" with her partner Michael Soames.

21s. (postage 8d.)

For Boys and Girls aged 8 - 12
ROCKETS, JETS, GUIDED MISSILES & SPACE SHIPS

by Jack Coggins and Fletcher Pratt

A fascinating and instructive guide to space travel. A handsome volume with many fine illustrations in colour and black-and-white.

4s. 6d. (postage 6d.)

THE POPULAR
Biggles Books
By Capt. W. E. Johns
BIGGLES IN THE GOBI

The latest Biggles book! There are thrills galore when Biggles and his Air Police fly to the rescue of eleven people smuggled out of Red China. Illustrated.

7s. 6d. (postage 4d.)

Also these Biggles books:

BIGGLES IN THE BLUE

BIGGLES SWEEPS THE DESERT

BIGGLES FAILS TO RETURN

BIGGLES IN THE ORIENT

SERGEANT BIGGLES, C.I.D.

BIGGLES' SECOND CASE

BIGGLES HUNTS BIG GAME

BIGGLES TAKES A HOLIDAY

BIGGLES GETS HIS MEN

ANOTHER JOB FOR BIGGLES

BIGGLES GOES TO SCHOOL

each 7s. 6d. (postage 4d.)

MAURICE WIGGIN

FISHING FOR BEGINNERS

Sound and sensible advice for the beginner—on basic tackle, hooks and floats; ground - baiting and casting; still water and running water. Illustrated.

8s. 6d. (postage 3d.)

100 BEST POEMS IN THE ENGLISH LANGUAGE

Chosen by Stephen Graham

Mr. Stephen Graham's personal choice of 100 poems—poems which have become an integral part of the language we speak.

10s. 6d. (postage 6d.

Margret Rey
SPOTTY

The story of a little bunny with blue eyes—and brown spots. With charming pictures in colour by H. A. Rey.

4s. (postage 3d.)

MARIE JOHNSON FORT

Flower Arrangements
For All Occasions

Preface by Julia Clements. A first-rate guide to the art of flower arrangement for large and small homes, parties, table decorations, flower shows. Illustrated with 32 reproductions in full-colour and 64 in monochrome, it offers boundless scope for the imaginative.

42s. (postage free)

MRS. BEETON'S COOKERY BOOK

More than 1,200 recipes and instructions on Home Management. 384 pages. Illustrated.

8s. 6d. (postage 5d.)

BING CROSBY
CALL ME LUCKY

Bing Crosby's own candid story of his life. Packed with entertaining stories of the best-known Hollywood personalities. Illustrated.

10s. 6d. (postage 5d.)

FLAP-BOOKS
by H. A. Rey

Children are entranced by the surprises concealed beneath the folding flaps in these delightful books. Illustrated in full colour.

WHERE'S MY BABY?
FEED THE ANIMALS
ANYBODY AT HOME?
HOW DO YOU GET THERE?

each 3s. 6d. (postage 3½d.)

PATIENCE STRONG BOOKS

Patience Strong's delightful prose-poems will be welcomed for their quiet wisdom and message of hope. They reflect a homely philosophy which draws its inspiration from the joys and sorrows of everyday life. Each volume is illustrated with beautiful camera studies.

SILVER LININGS
PATHS OF PROMISE
QUIET CORNER REFLECTIONS
SUNLIT BYWAYS
BEYOND THE RAINBOW
PATIENCE STRONG'S BOOK OF
HOME AND GARDENS

each 6s. (postage 3d.)

THE PLAIN MAN'S
GUIDE TO WINE
by RAYMOND POSTGATE

A sound, sensible and practical guide for the man—or woman—who wishes to be able to drink wine intelligently and not too expensively.

8s. 6d. (postage 3d.)

HORSES, HORSES, HORSES

Selected by Phyllis R. Fenner

Eighteen splendid short stories about horses. An excellent giftbook for youngsters.

8s. 6d. (postage 8d.)

GREAT TALES OF

TERROR AND THE SUPERNATURAL

Fifty-two hair-raising horror stories. Authors include Michael A r l e n, Thomas Hardy, Charles Dickens, O. Henry, W. W. Jacobs, Rudyard Kipling, Walter de la Mare, Edgar Allen Poe, Dorothy L. Sayers, H. G. Wells, Alexander Woollcott, etc.

18s. (postage 9d.)

Thrill-Packed Book For Boys!

EAGLE SPECIAL INVESTIGATOR

by Macdonald Hastings

Twenty-five exciting adventures ranging from "A Dive to the Bottom of the Sea" to "Flying the Atlantic." Sixty first-rate pictures, too!

8s. 6d. (postage 6d.)

BENNETT CERF

GOOD FOR A LAUGH

A grand collection of amusing anecdotes and jokes collected by the famous American columnist.

12s. 6d. (postage 5d.)

CRIMES OF LOVE, PASSION & POISON

Recalled by S. J. Coe

The gripping real-life stories of some of the most remarkable crimes of recent years.

8s. 6d. (postage 3d.)

ELIZABETH GOUDGE

The Heart Of The Family

" In many ways Elizabeth Goudge's loveliest book." An enchanting new novel which re-introduces the lovable Eliot family.

15s. (postage 6d.)

SELECTED

DOG STORIES

Edited by Era Zistel

An anthology of dog stories, both for those who like dogs and those who like good literature. Contributors include Hugh Walpole, A. A. Milne, John Galsworthy, Mark Twain, Zane Grey, Anatole France, etc.

10s. 6d. (postage 6d.)

GOOD HOUSEKEEPING'S

PICTURE RECIPE BOOK

Nearly 1,000 tested recipes for interesting yet inextravagant cookery. Over 300 excellent photographs, many in full colour.

17s. 6d. (postage 1s.)

GOOD HOUSEKEEPING'S

Picture Cake Making

Step-by-step instructions for mixing, baking, icing and decorating with recipes for all kinds of cakes, gateaux, sponges and patisseries. Over 500 photographs including 16 full-colour plates.

17s. 6d. (postage 1s.)

CAREERS FOR BOYS

by J. G. WATTERSON

A wealth of sensible information on some 85 careers for boys—including Agriculture, the Colonial Service, Law, Journalism, R a d i o Engineering, Surveying.

12s. 6d. (postage 5d.)

THE CONCISE ENCYCLOPÆDIA OF ANTIQUES

A comprehensive guide on every aspect of Antiques for every collector, connoisseur and art lover. It includes sections on Furniture, Carpets, Books, Silver, Jewellery, Paintings, Ceramics, Embroidery, etc. Profusely illustrated and lavishly produced.

42s. (postage free)

B.B.C. CHILDREN'S HOUR ANNUAL

Edited by

MAY E. JENKIN (" Elizabeth ")

A firm Christmas favourite, crowded with the lovable characters of both TV and Radio—including Andy Pandy, the Flowerpot Men, Milly-Molly-Mandy, Mr. and Mrs. Mumbo and many others. Packed with illustrations.

10s. 6d. (postage 1s.)

GOOD HOUSEKEEPING'S

BASIC COOKERY IN PICTURES

Compiled by the Good Housekeeping Institute. More than 700 photographs (many in full-colour) from which even the most inexperienced beginner can acquire a basic knowledge of cookery for the home.

10s. 6d. (postage 1s.)

Maiden Murders

by the

Mystery Writers of America Inc.

A collection of the **first** published short stories by some of the best-known mystery writers—among them, Ellery Queen, George Simenon, Brett Halliday, George Harmon Coxe, John Dickson Carr.

10s. 6d. (postage 11d.)

FOR BOYS AND GIRLS

SECRET IN THE SAND

by Mary E. Edmonston

Adventure and mystery for boys and girls aged 10 to 15 years. An exciting story with excitement and fun aplenty.

7s. 6d. (postage 5d.)

May We Help ?

If you have any difficulty in choosing your gift book perhaps you would like us to help you?

All you need do is to send us a brief description of the person for whom the books are intended (such as " 8s. 6d. book for an elderly lady," " 5s. book for a girl of six years," " 6s. book for a man interested in gardening ").

You may be certain that our experts will make a satisfactory choice; and, if you wish, we can post the books direct for you.

W & G FOYLE LTD

SIMPLE HERALDRY

by Iain Moncreiffe and Don Pottinger

A thoroughly informative guide to Heraldry—presented in an entertaining style, with a panoply of vivid colour on every page.

10s. 6d. (postage 5d.)

" The Doom of St. Trinian's "

SOULS IN TORMENT

by RONALD SEARLE

A new edition of Searle drawings—in which the creator of the girls of St. Trinian's announces the last hours of his infamous brood.

12s. 6d. (postage 6d.)

NEVILLE DUKE
Test Pilot

The thrilling life - story of Squadron-leader Neville Duke. A first-rate record of the boyhood dreams, war-time heroism and technical skill of one of the greatest exponents of supersonic flight. Illustrated.

12s. 6d. (postage 7d.)

HOW TO BE AN ALIEN
by George Mikes

For those who see the funny side of life. Chapters on hypocrisy, sex, tea, the weather, rudeness. Nicholas Bentley drew the pictures.

7s. 6d. (postage 3d.)

The Famous Tudor Edition
The Complete Works
OF SHAKESPEARE
Edited by PETER ALEXANDER

This splendid edition of Shakespeare's works includes an introduction summarising the facts of Shakespeare's life and his development as a dramatist; a glossary containing nearly 2,500 entries; and a valuable appendix on some of the problems encountered by Shakespeare's first printers. 1,376 pages.

15s. (postage 1s. 1d.)
de luxe edition 21s. (postage 1s. 1d.)

ENID BLYTON'S
SNOWDROP
STORY BOOK

Stories, verses, puzzles, strip-pictures. Many delightful illustrations.

10s. 6d. (postage 7d.)

These are, of course, only a few of the titles available at Foyles. We can supply all books reviewed, mentioned or advertised in any publication.

PEEPSHOW BOOKS

Here is something exciting for children. When the peepshow book is opened, by bending back the covers till they touch, coloured scenes appear with people, animals, trees and furniture—just as in a stage designer's set.

GOLDILOCKS AND THE THREE BEARS
Illustrated by Patricia Turner

THE SLEEPING BEAUTY
Illustrated by Roland Pym

PUSS IN BOOTS
Illustrated by Kathleen Hale

BEAUTY AND THE BEAST
Illustrated by Roland Pym

LITTLE RED RIDING HOOD
Illustrated by Patricia Turner

CINDERELLA
Illustrated by Roland Pym

THE BIRTH OF JESUS
Illustrated by R. T. Cowern

7s. 6d. each (postage 4d.)

SOCCER—THE WORLD GAME
by GEOFFREY GREEN

Introduction by Sir Stanley Rous. A great book for every soccer fan with brilliant reports of great Cup Finals, a cavalcade of the greatest players and lively comment on controversial football topics. With action photographs.

12s. 6d. (postage 4d.)

BETTY MACDONALD

Nancy and Plum

Betty Macdonald of "Egg and I" fame has written this delightful story of two little orphans' exciting escapades.
For ages 8 to 12 years.

6s. (postage 5d.)

ARTHUR RANSOME

SWALLOWS and AMAZONS

A new low-price edition of this immensely popular children's book. Illustrated.

5s. (postage 3d.)

A. C. WARD

ILLUSTRATED HISTORY OF ENGLISH LITERATURE

Volume One. CHAUCER TO SHAKESPEARE. A fascinating history of English writing, telling a truly absorbing story in engaging and attractive style. (The work will consist of three volumes but each volume is complete in itself.)

25s. (postage 8d.)

A Great New Reference Book

WORLD HISTORY
by J. C. Revill

A readable narrative and analytical account of great events, lives and institutions and a first-rate reference book of almost encyclopaedic character.

30s. (postage 1s. 4d.)

RICHARD BUCKLE

THE ADVENTURES OF A BALLET CRITIC

A brilliant and variegated pageant of London life—high, intellectual and low—by The Observer's ballet critic.

21s. (postage 1s.)

RECOMMENDED

THRILLERS

★

POST MORTEM by Guy Cullingford. A dramatic mystery; startlingly different.

9s. 6d. (postage 5d.)

HALF-MAST FOR THE DEEMSTER by George Bellairs. Murder in the Isle of Man.

9s. 6d. (postage 5d.)

THE CAUSE OF THE SCREAMING by David Elias. Introduces something new in detectives — a wise-cracking redhead with a great deal of glamour.

9s. 6d. (postage 5d.)

IN THE SHADOW by Austin Stone. The story of a murder that shocked all England.

10s. 6d. (postage 5d.)

13 WHITE TULIPS by Frances Crane. A murder mystery with a San Francisco setting.

9s. 6d. (postage 5d.)

KISS THE KILLER by Joseph Shallit. A fast-moving mystery story, packed with action, excitement—and humour.

9s. 6d. (postage 5d.)

THE IVORY GRIN by John Ross Macdonald. An exciting new thriller by a highly-praised mystery writer.

10s. 6d. (postage 5d.)

THE DEEP END by Fredric Brown. A fascinating thriller—a brilliant piece of mystery writing.

9s. 6d. (postage 5d.)

and some "TOUGH" THRILLERS

KISS ME DEADLY by Mickey Spillane. A new Mike Hammer thriller.

9s. 6d. (postage 5d.)

BRANDON TAKES OVER by Vernon Warren. A hard-hitting "private eye" on the track of Chicago thugs.

8s. 6d. (postage 5d.)

SHOOT TO KILL by Wade Miller. A fast-paced American murder mystery.

7s. 6d. (postage 5d.)

MUFFIN AT THE SEASIDE

by ANNETTE MILLS

A delightful fantasy introducing all Muffin's lovable friends. For children of seven to eleven.

6s. 6d. (postage 4d.)

THE PURPLE MUFFIN BOOK

Presented by Ann Hogarth

Stories and verses about Muffin and his friends, Muffin games and competitions, instructions for making a model television set, cartoon features and lots of other puzzles and stories.

6s. 6d. (postage 4d.)

★ A NEW ENID BLYTON ★

FIVE GO DOWN TO THE SEA

A thrilling new adventure of the famous "Five." Illustrated by Eileen Soper.

7s. 6d. (postage 4d.)

Also these other great "Five" books.

Each 7s. 6d. (postage 4d.)

FIVE ON A TREASURE ISLAND

FIVE GO ADVENTURING AGAIN

FIVE RUN AWAY TOGETHER

FIVE GO TO SMUGGLER'S TOP

FIVE GO OFF IN A CARAVAN

FIVE ON KIRRING ISLAND AGAIN

FIVE GO OFF TO CAMP

FIVE GET INTO TROUBLE

FIVE FALL INTO ADVENTURE

FIVE ON A HIKE TOGETHER

FIVE HAVE A WONDERFUL TIME

A Good-Humoured Leg-Pull

Call Me Florence

by JANE HOPE

A wickedly witty commentary on hospital life. A delightful gift-book— particularly for nurses.

6s. (postage 3d.)

TREMENDOUS SUCCESS !

THE ASCENT OF EVEREST

by Colonel Sir John Hunt

The authentic account of the British Everest Expedition's triumphant ascent. Illustrated with copyright photographs taken on the expedition.

25s. (postage 1s. 2d.)

WILLIAM JOYCE COWEN

LITTLE FRIEND

This story of a little French girl, Paulette, makes a particularly charming Christmas gift. It is a book which will be read and talked about for many years to come. Illustrated.

7s. 6d. (postage 3d.)

For Film - Fans!

PICTUREGOER FILM ANNUAL. A sparkling array of features, articles and pictures compiled by the staff of the popular **Picturegoer** magazine.

10s. 6d. (postage 6d.)

ROBERT SERVICE

SONGS FOR MY SUPPER

A new collection of vigorous verses by the author of "The Shooting of Dan McGrew."

10s. 6d. (postage 6d.)

For Girls and Boys Aged 11 to 16

THE POPULAR

PAMELA BROWN BOOKS

HARLEQUIN CORNER

An exciting holiday at a theatrical costumiers!

8s. 6d. (postage 6d.)

THE TELEVISION TWINS

The twelve-year-old Musgrove twins become television celebrities.

8s. 6d. (postage 6d.)

THE SWISH OF THE CURTAIN

The entertaining story of the Blue Door Theatre (made famous in the B.B.C. Children's Hour).

7s. 6d. (postage 7d.)

GOLDEN PAVEMENTS

A delightful story of the magic world of the theatre.

7s. 6d. (postage 6d.)

MADDY ALONE

More exciting adventures of the Blue Door Theatre Company.

6s. (postage 5d.)

BLUE DOOR VENTURE

The boys and girls of the Blue Door Theatre launch their own repertory company.

7s. 6d. (postage 6d.)

TO BE A BALLERINA

A wonderful collection of six Pamela Brown stories. Packed with fun and excitement.

7s. 6d. (postage 6d.)

FAMILY PLAYBILL

The story of an early Victorian theatrical touring family.

8s. 6d. (postage 6d.)

Books value £2 and over sent carriage paid in Great Britain

★ A NEW "JENNIFER" BOOK ★

John and Jennifer's Treasure Hunt

by Gee Denes

John and Jennifer seek buried treasure —and find a witch's broomstick and a singing toy. Illustrated with brilliant colour and black-and-white photographs.

6s. (postage 6d.)

SWITZERLAND'S AMAZING RAILWAYS

by CECIL J. ALLEN

The remarkable story of the fantastic skill, daring and sheer hard work that have gone into the Swiss railways' conquest of the Alps. With 200 beautiful illustrations of the magnificent scenic background.

25s. (postage 1s.)

FRANK RICHARDS

Billy Bunter's First Case

A great new laughable yarn of the boys of Greyfriars School.

7s. 6d. (postage 3d.)

Also in this series:—

BILLY BUNTER'S BRAIN-WAVE

BILLY BUNTER BUTTS IN

BILLY BUNTER'S POSTAL ORDER

BILLY BUNTER'S BANKNOTE

BILLY BUNTER'S CHRISTMAS PARTY

BILLY BUNTER OF GREYFRIARS SCHOOL

each 7s. 6d. (postage 3d.)

JANETTE SCOTT

ACT ONE

Thirteen-year-old stage and screen star Janette Scott tells the fascinating story of her life. Illustrated.

8s. 6d. (postage 5d.)

Royton E. Heath

ALPINE PLANTS UNDER GLASS

Sensible advice on the culture of alpine plants in an alpine house or frame. For the beginner and for those who would like to grow the more difficult and rarer plants.

12s. 6d. (postage 6d.)

Splendid New Edition of The Great Children's Classic

STRUWWELPETER

Illustrated by Janet and Anne Grahame Johnstone

"Takes on new life with the most attractive illustrations"—John O'London's Weekly. "This is a book for the unusual child"—Derek McCulloch.

6s. (postage 3d.)

DELIGHTFUL BOOKS FOR TINY TOTS

These four books make charming additions to Christmas stockings. Written by Dorothy Clewes and illustrated by Patricia Turner.

HENRY HARE'S EARTHQUAKE

HENRY HARE'S BOXING MATCH

HENRY HARE & THE KIDNAPPING OF SELINA SQUIRREL

HENRY HARE, PAINTER & DECORATOR

each 3s. 6d. (postage 2d.)

If any titles are out-of-print at time of ordering, suitable substitutes will be selected. Satisfaction is guaranteed.

JOHN ARLOTT'S
TEST MATCH DIARY
1953

The run-by-run record of the thrills and excitements of the historic 1953 Test Series. There are detailed statistics of every ball bowled in the series and a chapter on the personalities of both sides. Forty illustrations.

12s. 6d. (postage 5d.)

THE IMPRESSIONISTS AND THEIR WORLD

Introduction by BASIL TAYLOR

A large, beautiful volume with 96 full-page reproductions — 48 in glowing colour and 48 in monochrome. There are pictures by Manet, Monet, Renoir, Degas, Cezanne, Gauguin, Van Gogh, Toulouse-Lautrec and others. With notes on the paintings and biographies of the artists.

21s. (postage 1s.)

THE BOOK ABOUT
MOOMIN, MIMBLE AND LITTLE MY

by TOVE JANSSON

A delightful Christmas book for the younger generation of Moomin readers. Printed throughout in six colours and an ingenious succession of cut-outs reveals tantalising glimpses of pages to come.

8s. 6d. (postage 3d.)

THE STORY OF LITTLE BLACK SAMBO

by HELEN BANNERMAN

First published in 1899, this delightful little book has remained a popular favourite with all small children.

3s. 6d. (postage 2d.)

Also a larger edition with cut-outs
7s. 6d. (postage 4d.)

The WONDER BOOKS

This famous series is highly recommended for children's gift-books. All are lavishly - illustrated and handsomely produced.

THE WONDER BOOK OF
BIBLE STORIES

THE WONDER BOOK OF
THE FARM

THE WONDER BOOK OF
RAILWAYS

THE WONDER BOOK OF
SHIPS

THE WONDER BOOK OF
NATURE

THE WONDER BOOK OF
THE R.A.F.

each 12s. 6d. (postage 1s. 2d.)

FOR THE VERY YOUNG
PANTOMIME STORIES

All the favourite fairy stories of pantomime in full-colour pictures—The Sleeping Beauty, Aladdin, Little Red Riding Hood, Cinderella, etc.

5s. (postage 3d.)

THE PICK OF PUNCH

A grand selection of the best articles, cartoons and drawings from "Punch." Many colour illustrations.

12s. 6d. (postage 11d.)

Margret Rey
PRETZEL

The amusing story of a very l-o-n-g dachshund. A splendid children's book. Colour pictures by H. A. Rey.

4s. (postage 3d.)

THE GIRLS FROM ESQUIRE

A brilliant collection of stories and articles with thirty racy cartoons in the best "Esquire" tradition. Contributors include John Steinbeck, F. Scott Fitzgerald, James Jones, Budd Schulberg, Ilka Chase, Paul Gallico.

15s. (postage 1s.)

A Splendid Autobiography

SUITE IN FOUR MOVEMENTS

by ERIC COATES

The fascinating life-story of one of the best-loved personalities in contemporary English music.

16s. (postage 7d.)

H. P. PELLAPRAT'S
GOOD FOOD FROM FRANCE

Authentic French recipes for the woman who wishes to cook with flair and economy. It includes every necessary recipe—from a delicate omelet to superb puff-pastry.

12s. 6d. (postage 6d.)

FUN FOR FISHERMEN!

Walton's Delight

by GEORGE BRENNAND

Entertaining descriptions of the various types of fishermen—a witty, lively and knowledgeable volume. Illustrated by H. M. Bateman.

12s. 6d. (postage 6d.)

Foyles Bookshop is open daily from 9 a.m. to 6 p.m. (Thursdays 9 a.m.—7 p.m.)

PAUL GALLICO'S
THE SMALL MIRACLE

A beautiful new edition of Paul Gallico's famous story. Twenty-eight full-colour drawings by David Knight.

10s. 6d. (postage 6d.)

FOR BOYS AND GIRLS
THE STORY OF A NUTCRACKER

by Desmond MacCarthy and Bryan Guinness

A delightful adaptation of Hoffmann's tale of the little Nutcracker, on which the ballet Casse-Noisette was based. A charming and exciting story, enhanced by beautiful illustrations by Roland Pym.

9s. 6d. (postage 5d.)

THE WORLD-FAMOUS
MRS. BEETON'S
HOUSEHOLD MANAGEMENT

The great new up-to-date edition of Mrs. Beeton's famous cookery book, revised to meet present-day conditions and changing ideas and tastes. In addition to more than 4,000 recipes, "Household Management" includes important sections on the Nursery, the Home Doctor, Housework Etiquette, Labour - Saving Methods etc.; 1,680 pages; 350 illustrations.

42s. (postage free

RUDOLPH
THE RED-NOSED REINDEER
by Robert L. May

The phenomenally successful Rudolph the Red - nosed Reindeer makes charming Christmas gift — a delightfully produced book with brilliant full colour pictures.

2s. 6d. (postage 4d
" Pop - Up " edition with three dimensional " pop-up " pictures.

5s. (postage 6

GIVE BOOKS
FOR CHRISTMAS

FOYLES CHRISTMAS
BOOK GUIDE

A LIST OF SPECIALLY
RECOMMENDED TITLES
OBTAINABLE AT

The World's Greatest Bookshop

★ FOR BOOKS ★

119-125 Charing Cross Road
London, W.C.2

Telephone: Gerrard 5660 (16 lines)
Two minutes from Tottenham Court Road Station